We Can

by Anne Giulieri

I see a ball.
We can play.

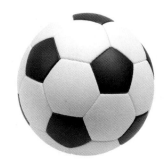

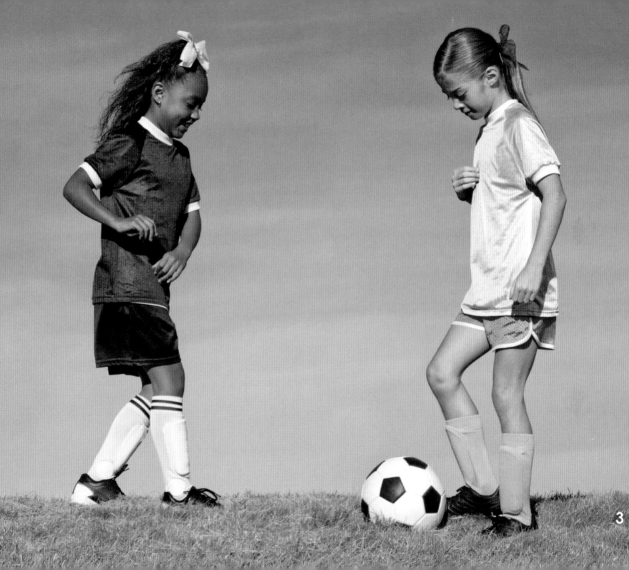

I see a swing.
We can play.

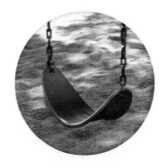

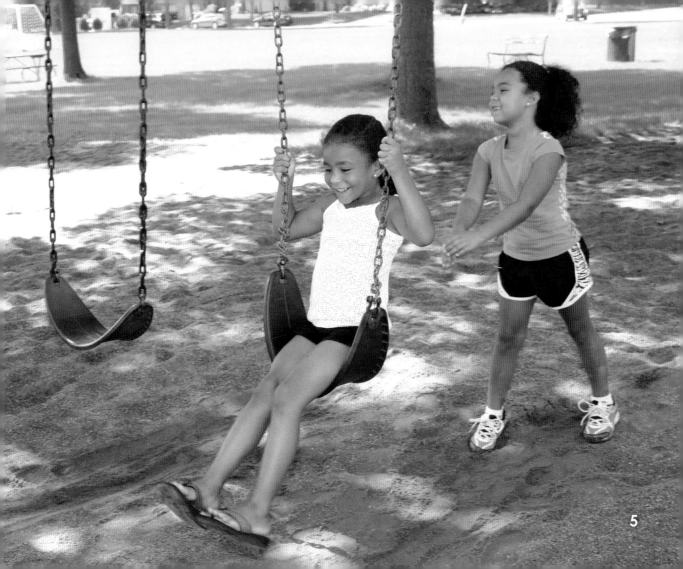

I see a slide.
We can play.

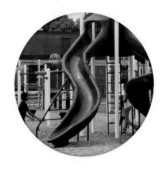

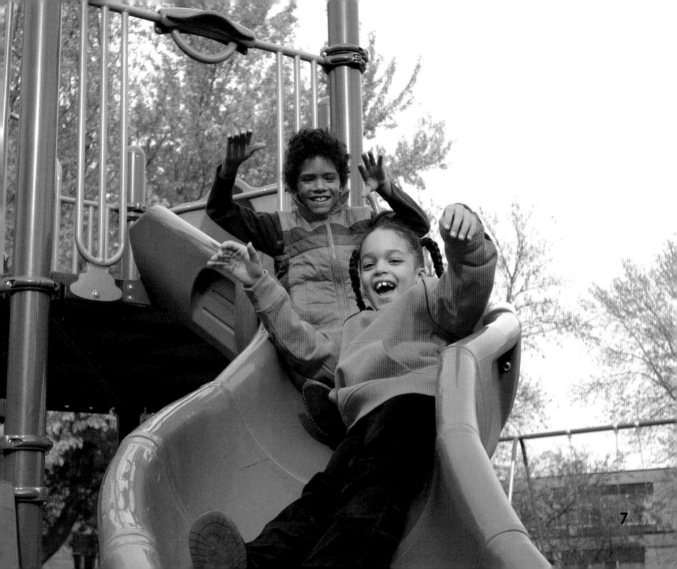

I see a block.
We can play.

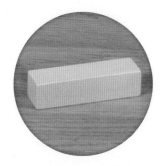

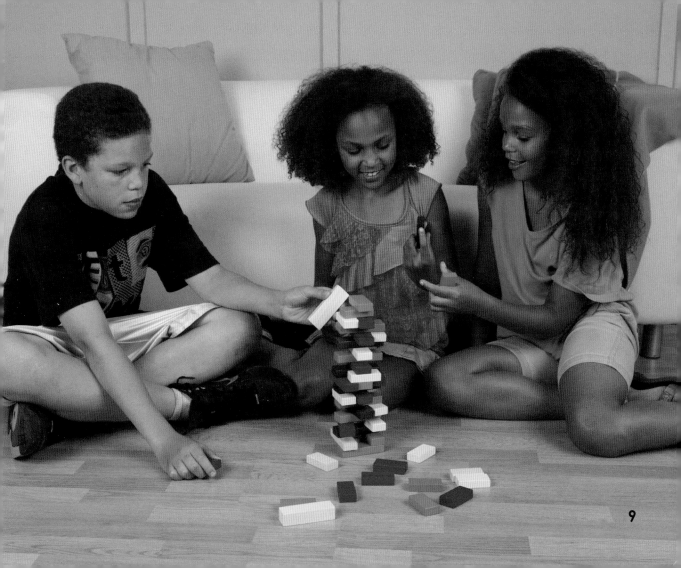

I see a dinosaur.
We can play.

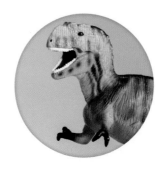

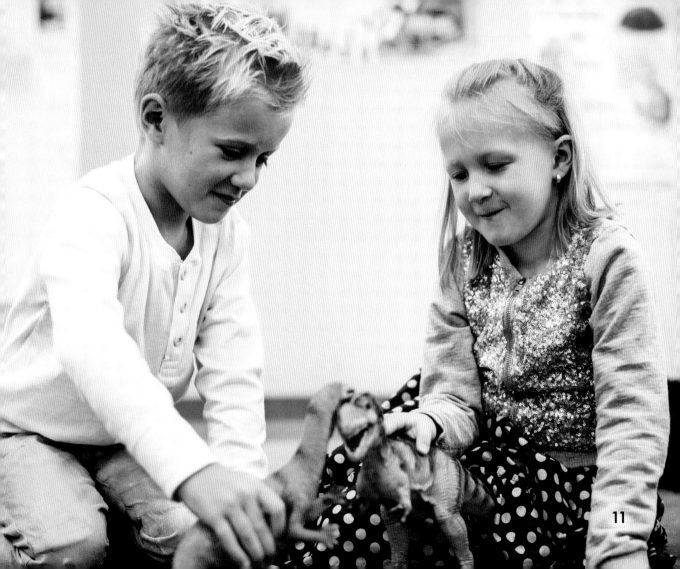

I see a bucket.
We can play.

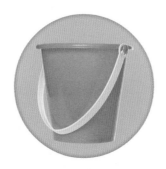

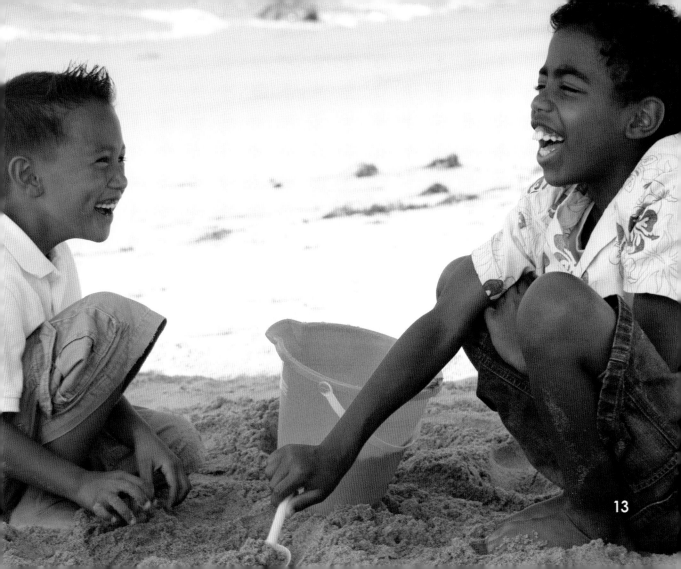

I see a game.
We can play.

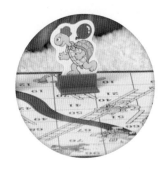

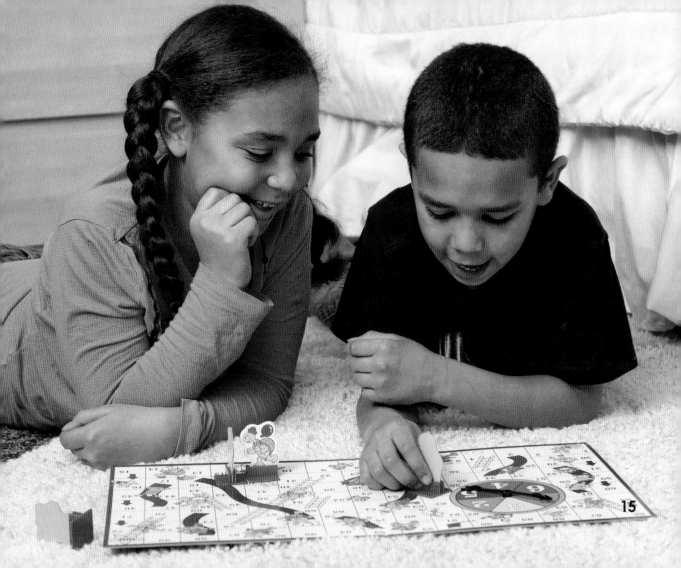

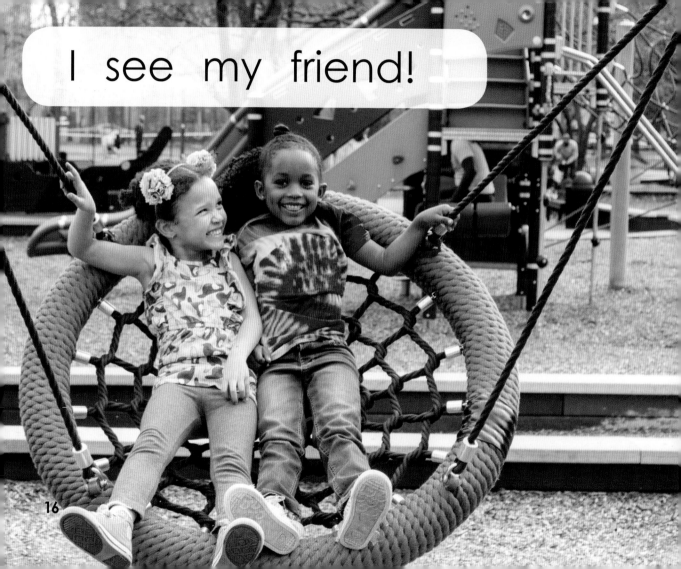

I see my friend!